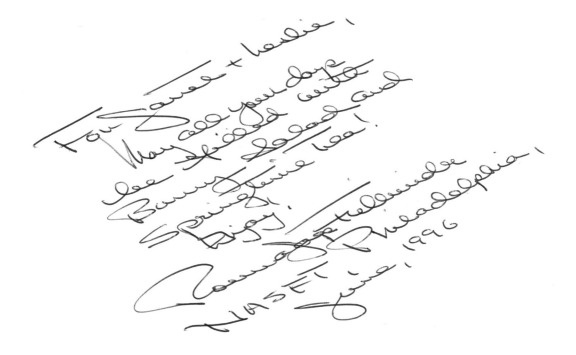

For Daniel + Leslie,
May all your days
be blessed with
Bernstein's food and
Spirit.

Clara Stellberger, Philadelphia,
NASET, June 1996

THE ADVENTURES OF
ROWENA & CARROT JAM
THE RABBIT

A CHILDREN'S STORY COOKBOOK

Carrot Jam The Rabbit is dedicated to the whole family at the Jam and Jelly Factory — all who mix and bake, fill and cap, wrap and pack, tie the lovely red bows, write the orders, concoct the recipes and then greet the customers with loving care. This is a tribute, as well as a thank you, to those people who create the wonderful aromas and special tastes we enjoy so much. Their devotion and skills touch us daily, producing a special magic and breathing life and heart into the factory where Carrot Jam was born.

Very special thanks . . .
to Sigrid Couch who perceived the essence of my concept and directed the
super support team which produced this book.
to Cameron Foster for her creative cooking talents with the recipes.
to Wilma Clark for her artistic eye in graphic design.
to Sharon Knapp for her ability to edit from a child's perspective.

Story copyright © 1990 by Rowena Jaap Fullinwider
Illustrations copyright © 1990 by Deborah G. Rogers

Designed by Clark Design Studio

A Children's Story-Cookbook Series
Published by Stanley Press

First Printing
Library of Congress Catalog Card Number: 95-71146
ISBN: 0-944345-12-3

Printed by Starr-Toof
Memphis, TN

THE ADVENTURES OF ROWENA & CARROT JAM
THE RABBIT

Written by Rowena Jaap Fullinwider
Illustrated by Deborah G. Rogers

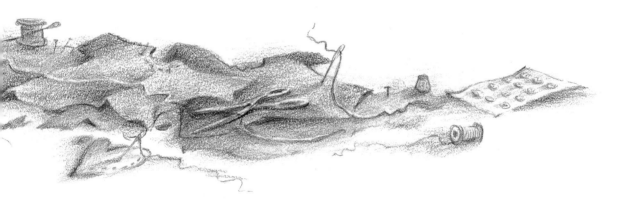

STANLEY PRESS
POST OFFICE BOX 11505
NORFOLK, VIRGINIA 23517

upon a time, there was a wonderful stuffed rabbit named Carrot Jam (C.J. for short). C.J. had the very good fortune to belong to a special little girl named Rowena. Because he was such a cuddly stuffed rabbit, C.J. was Rowena's very favorite toy. He had come to stay on her bed when she was just a tiny tot. Rowena loved to hold C.J. and hug him. The love that Rowena gave to C.J. was so caring and so warm that suddenly one night it sparked his heart and it began to beat. "How wonderful! I'm coming alive," thought C.J. "I can feel my heart beating and I can see." But although his heart could move, his arms and legs could not. "Oh," sighed C.J., "if only I could move and really be alive."

As Rowena grew older, C.J. learned that she needed him for many things. C.J. loved playing games with Rowena because the games they played were the closest he could come to being real. Sometimes Rowena played dress-up with C.J. He thought the outfits were quite silly. It was hard for him to pretend he was a ballerina because he was only a toy rabbit and could not dance. But when Rowena would hold him tightly and dance around and around, C.J. loved it! He wanted to dance and run and twirl around so much. A real rabbit could do these things.

Once a week, C.J. and Rowena would have a tea party. Rowena loved this most of all. She made these very special occasions. First, she would dust her tiny flower teacups and then carefully arrange everything on her little table. Best of all was the food — Bunny Salad, Tea Party Lady Fingers and Springtime Tea. C.J. enjoyed the tea parties but they made him a little sad too. "Oh, if only I were alive, I could really taste all these yummy things."

One day when they were in the garden having tea, Rowena said, "Gosh, I forgot to pick flowers for the table." She dashed off, leaving C.J. in charge. C.J. spied a fat puppy crawling under the hedge. C.J. watched as he wiggled and wiggled and then POPPED through the bushes.

The pup wanted to play, but of course C.J. couldn't. Just then the puppy smelled Tea Party Lady Fingers.

C.J. tried to wave his arms to scare the puppy but he was only a toy rabbit and his paws just wouldn't move. All of a sudden, the pup grabbed the tablecloth and yanked it. Over went all the tea party.

Rowena heard the noise and came running. "Oh no! Everything is ruined!" With tears in her eyes, Rowena gathered up her tea things. All C.J. could do was watch. "I could have stopped that puppy, if only I were alive!"

Since the tea party was spoiled, Rowena took C.J. up to her private tree fort.

The tree fort was a quiet place where they played "Let's Pretend" and shared many secrets. The floppy-eared rabbit was such a good listener that Rowena told him everything. No one else knew about the hole high in the old oak tree. It held Rowena's treasures — a small blue robin's egg that had fallen from a nearby nest, a shiny old coin and four beautiful feathers.

One day as the two friends sat under the tree, C.J. saw a bluejay high in the branches. He saw it move closer and closer to their secret hiding place. The bird poked his head in the hole and pulled out the shiny coin. C.J. could only watch as the bluejay flew away with the treasure. "If only I could have warned Rowena. It is so hard not to be alive."

C.J. and Rowena went everywhere together. It had been on one of their walks that Rowena had found the Jam and Jelly Factory. Bringing her grandmother's factory back to life had been Rowena's first big adventure. Now Rowena spent most of her time at the factory, but C.J. didn't mind because she was always happy there. Besides, she never left C.J. behind, not even for a moment. Everything in the factory seemed so alive that it made C.J. think about how much he wanted to be alive too. Oh, if only he could walk and talk like everyone else. Then he could help Rowena as Mr. Jellyfords Jam III did. Mr. Jam was the gentleman mouse who ran the factory. There was always a lot to do around the factory. It was hard just to sit watching Rowena and all the factory mice at work.

C.J. was afraid that he would NEVER get his wish to be alive. He felt so useless. The little stuffed rabbit had one other secret wish — he wanted to taste a real carrot. He knew that all rabbits were supposed to like carrots. They were even part of his name. Rowena's grandmother had made the stuffed rabbit for Rowena when she was just a little girl. Grandmother had named him Carrot Jam after one of her favorite recipes. She had even sown his initials C.J. in the tiny heart on his shirt. She knew that rabbits love carrots best of all. Becoming real and tasting a carrot were all that C.J. could dream about.

One day at the factory, Rowena decided to try to make Carrot Jam. C.J. thought this might be his big chance for carrot tasting. He became excited. Rowena put her friend in his special chair so he could see her as she cleaned and chopped all the carrots. C.J. really did not want to sit there another day while everyone else worked. But what could a toy rabbit do?

C.J. secretly hoped that one of the small slivers of carrots would fly his way, but everything was done so neatly that there didn't seem to be one extra piece. He watched Rowena lift the bowl of carrots and pour them into the huge pot with its warm mixture of sugar and spices. As she stirred the big pot, C.J.'s nose sniffed a delicious smell . . . AND . . .

THAT'S . . .

WHEN . . . IT . . .

HAPPENED!!

    As the little cook lifted the heavy pot from the candy stove, the pot began to tilt . . . and tilt some more.

THEN . . . SUDDENLY . . . SPLASH!!

C.J. felt something warm all over him. "What!! Could it be?? It must be!" He couldn't believe it.

"I've never felt anything warm before. Gosh, warm
feels good."

At that moment he knew he was covered with Carrot
Jam! "Now if only just this once I could taste it. But of
course, that's impossible for a toy rabbit."

OR . . . IS . . . IT?

As he sat in the jam this new warm feeling slowly crept over him . . .

AND

Grew

AND

Grew

AND

Grew

"What is happening to me? I feel so strange. I MUST BE COMING ALIVE!!"

C.J. looked down at himself. His arms moved, then his legs kicked! Even his nose twitched!!

"I'm alive — I'm REALLY ALIVE!" C.J. was so excited!

Rowena was a sight to see herself . . . all covered with sticky dripping jam.

Rowena couldn't believe her eyes.

"You're real! You're real! I can't believe you're REAL!!", exclaimed Rowena as she hugged him tightly. C.J. squirmed eagerly in her arms. Quickly Rowena put him on the floor, holding his paw as he tried to stand up. He shook one leg and then the other. Soon C.J. was whirling around the room with all the kitchen mice. "Now I can really be your friend. I can dance. I can eat at your parties. I can even help at the factory. I CAN DO ANYTHING!! Rowena called to all the little mice. "Let's have a party! We must celebrate!!"

Mr. Jellyfords Jam III agreed. "I'll get some ice cream. It'll be delicious with Carrot Jam on top. Let's have some Carrot Cone Cakes too."

One of the helper mice shouted excitedly, "I know how to make Wabbit Wrap-Ups. C.J. will really like those sandwiches." Another mouse said, "Don't forget that we like Fruit 'N Dip. It's fun to dip the fruit into the crunchy topping."

Rowena heard three mice talking about giving C.J. a present. She said, "Presents would be a great idea. It is his first "REAL ALIVE" birthday. We all want to make this a very special party."

In a short time, everything was ready. Everyone gathered around the kitchen table with their big bowls. Mr. Jam lit one candle on each cake. Rowena scooped big mounds of ice cream into each bowl. C.J. got his ice cream first.

They all waited and watched! C.J. took his first bite. His eyes got very big and bright with all the happiness he felt inside. A huge grin crept across his face. Carrot Jam was everything that he thought it would be, but

BEING ALIVE

WAS THE MOST WONDERFUL

ADVENTURE OF ALL!

THE END

ROWENA'S

ADVENTURES IN COOKING

Since C.J. is alive, he can now taste all the special foods that Rowena loves to serve. C.J. asked Rowena to share her recipes for a Tea Party and his Birthday Celebration with you. C.J. and Rowena hope that you will enjoy making and tasting these delicious recipes, too.

   Rowena says that learning to cook should be fun and always an adventure. C.J. agrees with her and hopes that you will have fun cooking these two menus.

HERE ARE A FEW IMPORTANT RULES TO REMEMBER:

1. Cook only with permission from an adult.
2. Read your recipe carefully before beginning to cook.
3. Get adult help with hot pans.
4. Be sure to use oven mitts when handling hot pans and jars.
5. Be careful around hot burners and ovens.
6. Be careful when using sharp knives.
7. Be sure to clean up the kitchen as you finish each recipe.
8. HAVE FUN!!!

FOR ADULTS TO READ !!

ROWENA'S TEA PARTY	C.J.'S BIRTHDAY CELEBRATION
TEA PARTY LADY FINGERS	WABBIT WRAP-UPS
BUNNY SALAD	FRUIT 'N DIP WITH CRUNCH
SPRINGTIME TEA	
PEANUT BUTTER CHOCOLATE TARTS	BUNNY-HOP MORNING SLUSH
	CARROT CONE CAKES

TEA PARTY LADY FINGERS

- *MAKES 8 SANDWICHES*
- YOU WILL NEED:

  spreading knife

  1 package of lady fingers
  any of the following:
      peanut butter
      apple butter
      pimento cheese spread
      deviled ham spread
      tuna salad

1. Carefully separate the top from the bottom of the lady fingers.
2. Spread the bottom with your choice of fillings.
3. Replace lady finger tops and separate into individual fingers.

Use your imagination!!!!!

BUNNY SALAD

- *MAKES 6 SALADS*
- YOU WILL NEED:

  wax paper
  rolling pin
  knife
  can opener

  one 1 lb. can of pear halves (6 halves)
  12 raisins
  6 red hot candies
  6 large marshmallows
  shredded lettuce
  6 carrot sticks

1. Place each pear half on a bed of shredded lettuce, round side up.
2. Cut each marshmallow in half vertically.
3. Cut one marshmallow half in 2 pieces.
4. Put each smaller piece between 2 pieces of waxed paper and roll out until they are flat and look like bunny ears. Repeat with remaining marshmallows.
5. Pat the pear half dry and place two ears on each half.
6. Put raisins where the bunny should have eyes.
7. Put the red hot where the bunny's nose should be.
8. Take the remaining marshmallow half and stick it to the back of the bunny for a tail.
9. Now arrange the carrot stick to look like the bunny is having a snack.

LITTLE MICE COOKING SCHOOL
LESSON 2:
cutting the Marshmallow
STEP 1.   STEP 2.   STEP 3.

SPRINGTIME TEA

- *MAKES 6 DRINKS*
- YOU WILL NEED:

  measuring cup
  sauce pan with top

  six cups white grape juice
  six ½ inch pieces of vanilla bean

1. Pour the juice into the saucepan and heat until it begins to boil.
2. Add the vanilla bean.
3. Cover the pan and let it "steep" or sit for 2-3 minutes.
4. It is now ready to enjoy hot or you could let it cool and pour it over ice. Both ways it's a lovely drink.

*You can substitute a cinnamon stick for the vanilla bean.

PEANUT BUTTER CHOCOLATE TARTS

- *MAKES 48 TARTS*
- YOU WILL NEED:

  four 12 cup mini muffin pans
  pot holders

  48 Reese's mini cups
  one 15 oz. roll of refrigerator cookie dough
  (peanut butter or sugar doughs work well)

1. Chill the Reese's cups so that the wrapper will come off easily.
2. Unwrap each piece and set aside.
3. Slice the dough into 12 even slices.
4. Cut each slice into 4 even pieces.
5. Place one piece in each mini muffin cup.
6. Bake 8-10 minutes in a 350 degree oven.
7. CAREFULLY remove the pan from the oven and immediately push one candy into each cookie.
8. Let cool in the refrigerator until the candy is firm.
9. Remove each tart carefully.

WABBIT WRAP-UPS

- *MAKES 12 WRAP-UPS*
- YOU WILL NEED:

  small mixing bowl
  spoon
  spreading knife

  2 tablespoons mustard
  3 tablespoons mayonnaise
  1 teaspoon chopped chives
  6 thin slices of smoked turkey
  6 thin slices of swiss cheese
  6 carrot sticks
  6 bread sticks

1. Mix mustard, mayonnaise and chives in a small bowl.
2. Spread each slice of turkey and cheese with the mixture.
3. Wrap 1 slice of turkey around 1 carrot stick. Make 2 more.
4. Wrap 1 slice of turkey around 1 bread stick. Make 2 more.
5. Wrap 1 slice of cheese around 1 carrot stick. Make 2 more.
6. Wrap 1 slice of cheese around 1 bread stick. Make 2 more.
7. Arrange 6 turkey and 6 cheese wrap-ups on a plate to serve.

You could use roast beef, salami or other cheeses as the wrappers and pickles, celery or cucumbers as the sticks to be wrapped. Have fun!

FRUIT 'N DIP WITH CRUNCH

- *MAKES 6 SERVINGS*
- YOU WILL NEED:

  large plate or platter
  2 bowls
  toothpicks
  baking sheet
  spoons

  Any combination of fresh or frozen
    fruits to make 3 cups.
  We like bananas, strawberries and
    pineapple the best.

DIP

1 cup sour cream
2 teaspoons honey
3 tablespoons brown sugar

1. Combine the above ingredients
   and mix well.

CRUNCH

2 tablespoons butter
1 tablespoon brown sugar
1 large shredded wheat biscuit
½ cup quick oats
¼ cup shredded coconut (optional)

1. Melt the butter and pour into a large
   bowl.
2. Add the brown sugar and stir until
   the sugar melts.
3. Add the oats and crumble the wheat
   biscuit. Mix well.
4. Spread this mixture onto a baking
   pan and cook 10 minutes in a 350
   degree oven. Stir well. Now add the
   coconut if using. Cook another 10
   minutes.
5. Carefully remove the pan from the
   oven and let cool. Store in an air
   tight container.

NOW arrange your fruit around a bowl of crunch and the bowl of dip on the platter.
Use the toothpicks if necessary to dip the fruit into the dip and then the crunch. Creamy
and crunchy all in one bite.

BUNNY-HOP MORNING SLUSH

- *MAKES 6 SMALL SERVINGS*
- YOU WILL NEED:

  blender or food processor
  knife
  spoon
  measuring spoon
  measuring cup

  2 cups chilled orange juice
  2 ripe bananas
  two 8 oz. cartons frozen vanilla
    yogurt
  1 cup fresh or frozen strawberries or
    blueberries
  ¼ cup wheat germ (optional)
  1 tablespoon vanilla extract

1. Pour orange juice into the blender or processor.
2. Peel and slice the bananas. Add to the juice.
3. Add the yogurt, fruit, wheat germ and extract.
4. Mix until the bananas are well blended.
5. Pour into glasses and enjoy with or without a straw.

CARROT CONE CAKES

- *MAKES 12 CONE CAKES*
- YOU WILL NEED:

  one 12 cup muffin tin
  medium mixing bowl
  small mixing bowl
  mixing spoon
  spreading knife

  12 flat bottom ice cream cones
  1 box (15 oz.) carrot cake mix
  1 can prepared cream cheese frosting
  2 tablespoons Rowena's Carrot Jam
    or any marmalade

1. Make the carrot cake mix by following the directions on the box.
2. Spoon the batter into the cones, filling three-quarters full.
3. Set each cone in a muffin cup for support when baking.
4. Bake for 30 minutes in a 350 degree oven. The cake should rise above the rim of the cones.
5. Carefully remove the cones from the oven.
6. Cool to room temperature.
7. Mix the frosting with the Carrot Jam and dip your cone-cake into the frosting with a swirling motion. If you need to, you can use a knife to help spread the frosting.

Order Today
Rowena's Children's Story-Cookbooks
Stanley Press
Post Office Box 11505
Norfolk, VA 23517

The fun begins when a delightful little girl, Rowena, rediscovers her grandmother's old Jam and Jelly factory. An elderly mouse, Mr. Jellyfords Jam III by name, helps Rowena find the magic needed to make the factory come to life again.

Please send _____ copies	@	$12.95 each	$_____
Plus postage	@	$3.50 each	$_____
VA residents add sales tax	@	$.58 each	$_____
		TOTAL	$_____

The adventure begins when Carrot Jam, Rowena's stuffed rabbit, wishes that he could be a real rabbit. Rowena cooks up a little magic and something wonderful happens.

Please send _____ copies	@	$14.95 each	$_____
Plus postage	@	$3.50 each	$_____
VA residents add sales tax	@	$.67 each	$_____
		TOTAL	$_____

Name: _____

Address: _____

City: _____ State _____ Zip_____

Make checks payable to Rowena's.

✂ -

Order Today
Rowena's Children's Story-Cookbooks
Stanley Press
Post Office Box 11505
Norfolk, VA 23517

The fun begins when a delightful little girl, Rowena, rediscovers her grandmother's old Jam and Jelly factory. An elderly mouse, Mr. Jellyfords Jam III by name, helps Rowena find the magic needed to make the factory come to life again.

Please send _____ copies	@	$12.95 each	$_____
Plus postage	@	$3.50 each	$_____
VA residents add sales tax	@	$.58 each	$_____
		TOTAL	$_____

The adventure begins when Carrot Jam, Rowena's stuffed rabbit, wishes that he could be a real rabbit. Rowena cooks up a little magic and something wonderful happens.

Please send _____ copies	@	$14.95 each	$_____
Plus postage	@	$3.50 each	$_____
VA residents add sales tax	@	$.67 each	$_____
		TOTAL	$_____

Name: _____

Address: _____

City: _____ State _____ Zip_____

Make checks payable to Rowena's.

Order Today
Rowena's Children's Story-Cookbooks
Stanley Press
Post Office Box 11505
Norfolk, VA 23517

The fun begins when a delightful little girl, Rowena, rediscovers her grandmother's old Jam and Jelly factory. An elderly mouse, Mr. Jellyfords Jam III by name, helps Rowena find the magic needed to make the factory come to life again.

Please send _____ copies @ $12.95 each $_____
Plus postage @ $3.50 each $_____
VA residents add sales tax @ $.58 each $_____
TOTAL $_____

The adventure begins when Carrot Jam, Rowena's stuffed rabbit, wishes that he could be a real rabbit. Rowena cooks up a little magic and something wonderful happens.

Please send _____ copies @ $14.95 each $_____
Plus postage @ $3.50 each $_____
VA residents add sales tax @ $.67 each $_____
TOTAL $_____

Name: _____
Address: _____
City: _____ State _____ Zip_____

Make checks payable to Rowena's.

Order Today
Rowena's Children's Story-Cookbooks
Stanley Press
Post Office Box 11505
Norfolk, VA 23517

The fun begins when a delightful little girl, Rowena, rediscovers her grandmother's old Jam and Jelly factory. An elderly mouse, Mr. Jellyfords Jam III by name, helps Rowena find the magic needed to make the factory come to life again.

Please send _____ copies @ $12.95 each $_____
Plus postage @ $3.50 each $_____
VA residents add sales tax @ $.58 each $_____
TOTAL $_____

The adventure begins when Carrot Jam, Rowena's stuffed rabbit, wishes that he could be a real rabbit. Rowena cooks up a little magic and something wonderful happens.

Please send _____ copies @ $14.95 each $_____
Plus postage @ $3.50 each $_____
VA residents add sales tax @ $.67 each $_____
TOTAL $_____

Name: _____
Address: _____
City: _____ State _____ Zip_____

Make checks payable to Rowena's.